PERFECT

COOL

Kermit

By Kermit the Frog
as told to Anna Ludlow & Charlie Gardner
Designed by Mandy Norman

THE COOL ZONE

Kermit the Frog here welcoming you to the **Perfectly Cool Kermit Book.** Now in all my time with the Muppets I have been called upon to introduce many extraordinary guests. But I have never before been asked to introduce 'A Cool, Green Book'. Anyway, here goes . . .

It's shiny and bright and made of paper, with 32 pages of action-packed excitement. Please give a big, big Muppet Show welcome for the un-putdownable **Perfectly Cool Kermit Book.**

Yeeeeeaaaaaahhhhhhh!

Froggy ... that was so uncool. Don't you think if you're going to introduce a book like this you should make it COOOOOL? If it were me introducing the book, I'd say: 'This book is so cool ~ on a hot summer's day you can use it to fan yourself!' Wocka - wocka!

Fozzie ... that is, without doubt, the stupidest thing you have ever said. Now will you let me get on with this book please?

Welcome to the **Perfectly Cool Kermit Book,** with lots of things that will help you hang on to your cool while all about you are losing theirs. There's some stuff on what it's like to be Cool and Green, being Cool at sport, and being Cool with your friends and family. Oh, and there's a really neat bit about 'Hanging Out'.

Ladies and Gentlemen, a book so cool that you can use it to fan yourself on a hot summer's day! I give you the **Perfectly Cool Kermit Book!**

FRIENDS

I like to think of my friends as my second family ~ the one I picked! I wouldn't be able to get through the day without my friends ~ especially the ones who buy me lunch. Here's a little portrait gallery of the ones who remember my birthday, at least . . .

JOKE TRAIL
JOKE TRAIL
JOKE TRAIL

This is Fozzie Bear. He's my oldest friend ~ but not as old as his jokes!

MUPPETS TONIGHT

Clifford is the Professor of Hip and the Coolest of the Cool. But hey, he learned it all from me!

Is it a bird?
Is it a plane?
No, it's the
Great Gonzo!

Here's the world's greatest
Party Animal. In fact, he's
the world's greatest Animal,
full-stop. We're great
friends ~ but I'm glad he
doesn't live next door!

And of
course, where
would I be
without the
inimitable
Miss
Piggy?

Better off!
Hah, hah,
hah, hah,
hah!

PLAY IT COOL

I used to find it easier to laugh
at Fozzie's bad jokes than to talk to girls.
I never thought much about what the ideal girlfriend
should be like, but Miss Piggy changed all that ...
and now, everyone wants to know ~ *are* we
having a relationship or *aren't* we.

Well ... let me set the record straight. I am an amphibian. Miss Piggy is a pig. We have a naturally **ampiguous** relationship. This means, my life wouldn't be the same without her and she wouldn't be where she is today without me.

And **you** shouldn't believe anything you see in the papers. Photos can be computer-enhanced ~ I believe Miss Piggy paid a considerable amount for this one.

The **DAILY GOSSIP**

Issue 1

Full story inside!

MISS PIGGY GETS HER FROG!

Knowing Miss Piggy has done a lot for me ~ I now have a very good idea of what to look for and what **NOT** to look for in a girlfriend ...

LOOK FOR A GIRL WHO ...	WATCH OUT FOR A GIRL WHO ...
Loves you for what you are	Loves you because you're a star
Likes your favourite sport	Has more talent than you at your favourite sport
Always likes your presence	Only likes expensive presents
Likes you because you're funny	Wants you for your money
Is always happy to lend you a hand	Always wants the upper hand

Whatever you do, don't get on the wrong side of a girl who is taller than you, with a talent for self defence!

PRIZE PAD

Working in New York City is great ~ I love it. But, I'm a frog, and sometimes I miss my childhood days, just sitting on a lily-pad, playing my banjo and listening to my frog friends croaking away to each other in the swamp.

Whenever I feel that way, I head back to my New York hideaway ~ my *frog-pad*. It's important to have your own place, where you can hang out, be yourself and just *keep cool!*

My favourite place is a **cool, green zone,** where there are cool, green leaves underfoot and lily-pads floating in cool, clear water ~ my bathroom!

I love to pick up my banjo and play the tape I made of my frog friends singing together on a summer evening. Pretty soon, I feel like I'm right back home, **in my natural habitat!**

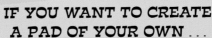

IF YOU WANT TO CREATE A PAD OF YOUR OWN ...

● **Be bold** ~ experiment by decorating your room with colours that reflect your **personality.**

● Don't let friends like mine experiment for you! I made that mistake once ~ I'll never let **Gonzo** choose wallpaper for me again!

● If you can't hire a professional to paint your walls ~ don't hire **Randy & Andy.** They give new meaning to adding a **splash** of colour!

MAKE YOUR PAD A COOL ZONE!

TIME OUT

'Work hard, play hard,' has never been a motto for the Muppets. With us, it's more like, 'Work ... do we have to? Play ... all the time!' Whatever you do, it's important to take time out to do the things you love. These are just a few of my favourite hobbies.

SCUBA DIVING

Here's a handy holiday dress tip. You'll always look cool in a wet suit and never look wet in a cool suit! So even though I don't really need one, I always wear a wet suit when Piggy and I go diving in the **Caribbean.** Never have seen the sense in buying flippers, though!

PAINTING

A very cool hobby, even if you can barely draw the curtains! You may never sell anyone a picture in your lifetime, but hey, neither did **Van Gogh!**

HIKING

Hiking is a really **cool** hobby ~ you get to be out in the fresh air, enjoy beautiful scenery and sometimes, get soaked to the skin. It makes me feel like I'm right back home! But try persuading your **friends** to come along! I thought I had once, but then I showed them where we were going on the map.

Suddenly, Miss Piggy remembered some shopping she had to do. Rizzo was consumed by hunger and had to go and get a pizza. Clifford was called away by a mysterious, urgent phone call on his mobile. Only Gonzo wasn't discouraged. 'That looks really cool,' he said. 'I'll try out my new **rocket-powered** hang-glider and meet you there!'

IN THE GROOVE

Music has always been a very important part of my life and its coolest moments will stay in my memory forever. The way that people enjoy so many different types of music is really cool. Even Miss Piggy's singing is probably music to somebody's ears! So what's the secret of being *musicool*? The 'key' is to express your personality with the right style of music. For example …

The coolest music ever composed is the perfect partner for one of the coolest guys I've ever met ... **Zoot.** This dude can play a mean saxophone as well as a generous clarinet and a very friendly flugelhorn. Multi-talented and **awesome!**

RAP

My man **Rizzo** is a rapping Rat,
He can rap like a dog or a real cool cat,
He raps in his sneakers and his baseball cap,
So rock to the beat of the Master **Rat Rap!**

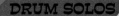

DRUM SOLOS

Animal has that great quality that all cool drummers have ~ absolutely no musical talent whatsoever! To be this good takes practice, but life for Animal is just one long drum solo, anyway, so that's easy. He may look angry when he's beating those **tom-toms,** but that's what cool drumming is all about. He never stops playing. Sometimes, I wish he would!

SMOOTH 'N' EASY

Music is like peanut butter ~ some like it crunchy, but I prefer it 'smooth 'n' easy'. This Passionate Pig, this Mellow Fellow and these Pop-Music Porkers all manage to make their music sound effortless ~ though in the case of *Pigzone*, that's because they didn't put in any effort in the first place!

pig zone

KMUP records

BOY BANDS

After *Take Fat* split up, record producers started searching for the next Boy Band sensation, until one finally discovered the talent of **Randy and Andy**. 'You can't sing, you can't act, you're completely bald, and your acting's really hammy!' he told them. 'I'm going to make you the biggest Boy Band ever!' *Pigzone* was born and the rest is history ~ including their chart bottoming single, 'Sack me for a reason, and let the reason be … I don't know, got any suggestions?'
This song's too hard!

Tragic, romantic, wildly melodramatic and completely over-the-top ~ well that's enough about **Miss Piggy**. Oh, did you think I was talking about opera? Few styles of music can come close to matching the theatrical splendour of the **Grande Pig** herself, but the opera, at least, has a decent 'shout' at it. *Pigoletto* and *The Marriage of Pigaro* have always been particular favourites of Piggy.

CROONING

Italian is the language of love, and it's a language which **Johnny Fiamma** speaks fluently. Those passionate eyes, that love-lorn face, that tragic smile ~ this man was born to be a romantic ballad singer. Not many artistes can sing **'moon, June, spoon and croon'**, in the same verse and still make you weep over your soup ~ unless it's onion soup, of course! Johnny left his heart in San Francisco, that's for sure, and I just hope he finds it again, one day.

Whatever your taste, the way you groove can be smooth!

GET YOUR KIT ON!

You don't have to be the world's greatest athlete to be cool at the sports you like. After all, I'm not 6' 6" with rippling muscles and the body of an athlete, but I still have a cool time playing all these sports with my friends.

FOOTBALL

To be perfectly cool at football, you must become the **team mascot**. You get to wear the first team strip, you get to travel with the team and, hey, you even get to play for the team ... during the warm-up. But you don't get tired, injured or muddy. You just stay cool!

BASKETBALL

The last time I played basketball, Statler and Waldorf yelled, *'Green guys can't jump!'* at me from the crowd. I was hopping mad!
A cool move to stop your opponents from scoring is to jam one of your defenders in the net hoop. Animal always volunteers, mainly because he likes to get a great beat going by banging his feet on the backboard!

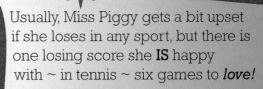

Usually, Miss Piggy gets a bit upset if she loses in any sport, but there is one losing score she **IS** happy with ~ in tennis ~ six games to *love!*

I once had to referee a match between Randy and Andy. They both wanted to stand at the same end because the sun was in their eyes! And every time the score reached 'Deuce' they stopped playing and had a drink of orange! It took a whole afternoon just to play one set! **That job was too hard!**

CYCLING

A lot of people think I look really cool on a bike ~ something to do with the webbed feet, I would guess. But, hey, you should see their faces when I show them how I can ride a bike through a river ... it's just the coolest **amphibious vehicle** you will ever see!

IT'S NOT EASY BEIN' GREEN

When you're born green, like me, there are certain considerations you can't ignore ~ green issues, the greenhouse effect, and Miss Piggy being green with envy!

Part of my mission in Muppet-life is to preach the gospel of green, which says ...

DO	DON'T
Recycle old newspapers	Recycle old jokes
Save energy	Save yesterday's pizza
Be green	Be blue

The Green Party often asks me to be their spokesfrog, but I have to refuse. I'm already Chairman of another environmentalist party, the **Perfection Is Green Party** (P.I.G.), which has naturally attracted the perfect candidate to run for President of the U.S.A. ~ Miss Piggy!

It's cool bein' GREEN!

ISLAND HOPPING

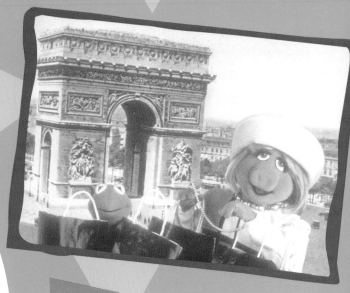

The success of the Muppet movies and shows has forced me to travel all over the world ~ this year I've flown 30,000 miles already. Well, I have to do something with all those airmiles Piggy keeps clocking up on my credit card!

Directing all the Muppet productions is wonderful because it takes me to all the cities and countries I love best.

PARIS

Paris is the fashion capital of the world, so Piggy always makes us **'drop-in'** there on our way back to New York. It's supposed to be a holiday, but the reality is that I'm dragged from one Fashion House to another while her Pigness tries on every new outfit and samples every new perfume. I even have to pay for all the taxis!

LONDON

London is a really cool city, but for an American tourist, the names on the London tube map can be very confusing at first. If you've yet to visit this wonderful city, here are a few words of advice ... You won't find any clowns at **Oxford Circus** and it's nowhere near Oxford! There's not much bread in **Baker Street,** and if you go to **Bond Street,** don't expect to see James!

But there are plenty of great places to visit. Here are my **Top Five** favourite hang-outs when I'm in the city.

Madame Tussauds ~ I love standing next to my lookalike and seeing if Piggy can pick out the real me. One time she went off with the dummy and didn't notice the difference until it wouldn't pay for lunch!

Kew Gardens ~ Frog Paradise!

Buckingham Palace ~ Pig Paradise!

Natural History Museum ~ It's great to meet up with hundreds of my ancestors ~ even if they don't have much to say for themselves anymore!

Open-Top Bus Tour ~ The best way to see London and certainly very cool ~ especially on a windy day!

PERFECT PARADISE?

DESERT ISLAND DISASTER

If you want a really unusual holiday, go away with friends like mine. None of us will forget the time when **Gonzo** took us all on holiday to a beach house on a remote, uninhabited island.

As we came in to land, we were astonished when Gonzo put on his rollerblades and said, 'There's no airport on this island, but don't worry, I'm going to make a really neat landing, right on the patio, with me as the aeroplane's wheels!' Thankfully, we all survived, but the house didn't, so we spent the holiday living on the beach!

Why not try this at home?
Put up a hammock or deck chair in your room.
Add a few potted plants and a bright yellow lamp, play
some music that sounds like the sea and there you go.

Be careful how far you go with the realism.
I made the mistake of telling Rizzo that I wanted to be able
to feel the waves crashing onto the shore, so the little guy
went and threw a bucket of water all over me!

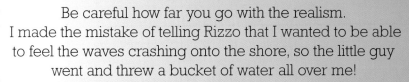

HANGING OUT

Hanging out with friends can be really *cooool.* But how do you find the right place to hang out?

Almost anywhere will do, as long as you can be with your friends, be yourself and **BE SEEN.**

BREAKFAST AT PEPE'S

The coolest way to start the day,
Is breakfast served by our man Pepe.

NEW YORK DINER

Fozzie and I love spending Saturday afternoons in **New York diners.** Fozzie tries out all his new jokes on me, while I listen carefully ... to the jukebox.

STEPPING OUT

If you want to **be seen,** choose a place where the reporters hang out, looking for stars to photograph. A TV studio is usually a good bet. Put on a pair of **cool shades** and hold your hand up in front of all the cameras. Before long, someone is bound to take your picture. If you make it into the papers the next day, you're on your way to being a star!

THE COMEDY CLUB

We're always on the lookout for **new talent,** especially when we hang out at comedy clubs in downtown Manhattan. Fozzie is always looking for someone's jokes to steal, Miss Piggy is always hoping to meet a film director and Rizzo is always on the look out for a pizza.

HANGING ON

Just remember, if someone suggests you 'hang out' together, this is **NOT** what they mean!

HAPPY FAMILIES

My Muppet
friends are just
like a family to me.
They do so many crazy
things, it sometimes drives
me mad. But I've found that if
I keep believing in them, it helps
them realise their dreams.

Do you wonder why your family
behave the way they do?
Do they always do the things that
embarrass you most at
the worst possible moment?

Don't despair ~ the very
thing that makes you mad
may make them a
star one day, just like
these dreamers ...

The father who suddenly breaks into song, just as your friend arrives at the door. The song is awful and he only knows half the words. But who says you have to **finish** a song to be a famous singer?!

The sister who always takes charge, is determined to get what she wants, believes she has enormous talent, whether it's true or not, and **never** gives up. But deep down, she knows she's less than perfect ~ that's why she spends so long in the bathroom! She has almost everything she needs to be a movie star!

The uncle who makes you listen to all his jokes. He never gives up ~ it may drive you insane, but he knows that one day, he'll make you laugh. Without you, how can he become a top comedian?!

The brother whose idea of fun is to dive into the garden pond from the bedroom window. Everything he does is wildly inappropriate. But his courage and hopeful dreams of heroism are all he needs to become the most **memorable** stuntman in history!

THE DREAM

People often ask me how it all started ~ how I met my Muppet friends and how that medley of mirth and magic called *The Muppet Show* began.

As a young frog, I dreamed of getting into **show business.** But when you live in a marsh, you don't meet a lot of movie directors on the look-out for talent, so I wasn't exactly swamped with offers. My father once said, 'Son, better to be a success at one single thing in life than a failure in many.' I was already pretty good at swimming, and I could play the banjo too, so I set off for **Hollywood** with high hopes.

You'd think that a frog with a **banjo** would be in great demand, but funnily enough, playing my banjo whilst riding a unicycle and juggling with fire clubs only paid enough for one meal a day.

When I met Fozzie Bear in a nightclub, I realised he was the **perfect partner** ~ doing a double act with a bear who can't tell jokes is the best way to eat in style ~ you get enough food thrown at you to last a week!

RICH & FAMOUS

Before long, Fozzie and I had met lots of other crazy characters. Their acting talents were ... well, unique. I'd surrounded myself with a bunch of numbskulls, but they all had one thing in common ~ a dream of stardom.

None of us had much chance of making it on our own, but together, I believed we could make our dreams come true . . .

We went to see Hollywood's greatest movie director, Lew Lord. He could spot talent in a moment, so he cried, 'Prepare the Rich and Famous contract for Kermit the Frog and company!'
At last, we'd made it!

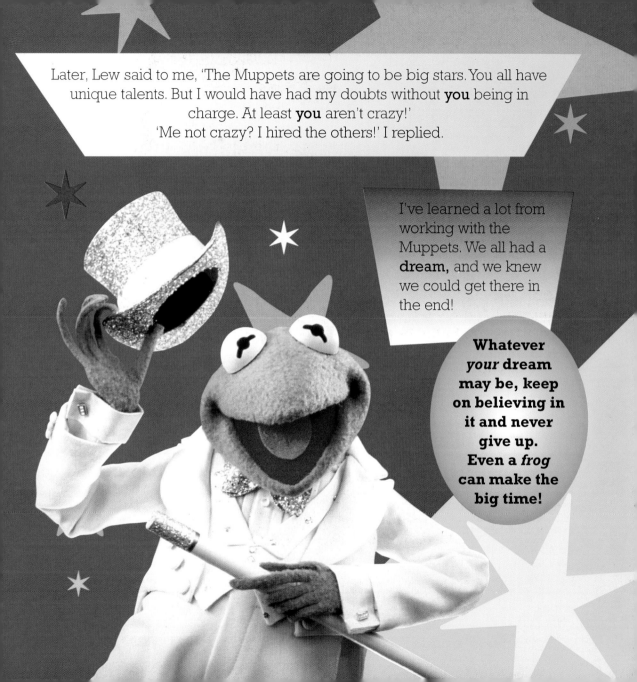

Later, Lew said to me, 'The Muppets are going to be big stars. You all have unique talents. But I would have had my doubts without **you** being in charge. At least **you** aren't crazy!'
'Me not crazy? I hired the others!' I replied.

I've learned a lot from working with the Muppets. We all had a **dream,** and we knew we could get there in the end!

Whatever *your* dream may be, keep on believing in it and never give up. Even a *frog* can make the big time!